Harcourt
Health and Fitness

Assessment Guide
Grade 3

D1472677

Harcourt
SCHOOL PUBLISHERS

Orlando • Austin • New York • San Diego • Toronto • London

Visit *The Learning Site!*
www.harcourtschool.com

Printed in the United States of America

ISBN 13: 978-0-15-355147-5
ISBN 10: 0-15-355147-X

2 3 4 5 6 7 8 9 10 073 15 14 13 12 11 10 09 08 07 06

Grade 3—Contents

© Harcourt

Assessment Guide Overview

In *HARCOURT HEALTH AND FITNESS*, the assessment program, like the instruction, is student-centered. It allows all learners to show what they know and what they can do, thus providing you with ongoing information about each student's understanding of health. Equally important, the assessment program involves the student in self-assessment, offering you strategies for helping students evaluate their own growth.

The *HARCOURT HEALTH AND FITNESS* assessment program is based on the Assessment Model in the chart below. The model's framework shows the multidimensional aspect of the program. The model is balanced between teacher-based and student-based assessments.

The student-based strand of the Assessment Model involves assessments that invite the student to become a partner in the assessment process and to reflect on and evaluate his or her own efforts. The student-based strand consists of two components: Student Self-Assessment and Portfolio Assessment.

The teacher-based strand of the Assessment Model involves assessments in which the teacher typically evaluates a piece of work as evidence of the student's understanding of the health content and of his or her ability to think critically about it. The teacher-based strand also consists of two components: Formal Assessment and Performance Assessment.

There is a fifth component in the *HARCOURT HEALTH AND FITNESS* assessment program: Daily Assessment. This essential component is listed in the center of the Assessment Model because it is the "glue" that binds together all the other types of assessment.

HARCOURT HEALTH AND FITNESS ASSESSMENT MODEL

STUDENT SELF-ASSESSMENT	PORTFOLIO ASSESSMENT
DAILY ASSESSMENT	
FORMAL ASSESSMENT	PERFORMANCE ASSESSMENT

Description of Assessment Components

Daily Assessment and Classroom Observation
Daily Assessment is central to the assessment program. Ultimately, it is the daily events that are observed and recorded that provide the most comprehensive assessment of student growth. *Harcourt Health and Fitness* provides several ways of helping you assess daily student progress.

- In the *Student Edition* and *Teacher Edition* every lesson in Grades 3–6 ends with a Lesson Summary and Review. These features provide a mix of factual recall, critical thinking, and skill questions.
- In this *Assessment Guide* a Life Skills Observation Checklist (page 6) and a Character Traits Observation Checklist (page 7) can help you evaluate students' skills in health.

Student Self-Assessment
Student Self-Assessment encourages students to reflect on and monitor their own gains in health knowledge, development of Life Skills and Character Traits, and changes in attitude.

- In the *Student Edition* and *Teacher Edition*, Personal Health Plans, Life Skills, and Character Traits are features of every chapter. These features encourage students to reflect on what they have learned and apply their new knowledge to their lives.
- In this *Assessment Guide* you will find a Health Habits Checklist (page 9) for students to use in assessing their current level of wellness. The Individual Self-Assessment Checklist (page 10) and the Team Self-Assessment Checklist (page 11) can be used to aid students in reflecting on their performance.

Portfolio Assessment
Students make their own portfolios in Portfolio Assessment. Portfolios may also contain a few required or teacher-selected papers.

- In the *Student Edition* and *Teacher Edition* every chapter includes a wealth of activities that result in products that can be included as portfolio items.
- In this *Assessment Guide* are support materials (pages 12–16) to assist you and your students in developing portfolios and in using them to evaluate growth in health.

Formal Assessment
Formal Assessment can help you reinforce and assess students' understandings of ideas developed in each chapter. Chapter Reviews and Tests require students to reflect on, summarize, and apply chapter concepts.

- In the *Student Edition* and *Teacher Edition* each chapter ends with a Chapter Review and Test Preparation.
- In this *Assessment Guide* is a test for each chapter (beginning on page 19). Answers are shown in reduced form in the *Teacher Edition*, as well as in the Answer Key on pages 74–85.

Performance Assessment
Health literacy involves more than just what students know. It is also concerned with how they think and how they do things. The Chapter Project is a performance task that can provide you with insights about students' knowledge, skills, and behaviors.

- Chapter Projects are found on pages 56–61 of this *Assessment Guide*. You may assign a project at the beginning of the chapter, and students can work on the project individually or in teams throughout the chapter.
- Students can assess their own performance on a project by using the Student Project Summary Sheet found on page 18.

Daily Assessment and Classroom Observation

In *HARCOURT HEALTH AND FITNESS*, "child watching" is a natural and continual part of the evaluation process. Observation checklists are provided on pages 6 and 7 for recording student performance on six Life Skills and six Character Traits that are emphasized in the program. Indicators to help you evaluate each skill and trait appear on the checklists.

Life Skills

❑ **Make Responsible Decisions**—evaluating alternatives to decide on the wisest thing to do

❑ **Refuse**—using strategies to effectively react to peer pressure so as to avoid a risky action

❑ **Resolve Conflicts**—using strategies to effectively communicate and compromise in order to find solutions to problems or to avoid violence

❑ **Manage Stress**—acting to relieve the symptoms of stress when physical, intellectual, emotional, or social needs are not met

❑ **Communicate**—transmitting information, ideas, needs, feelings, or requests in a form that aids interpretation

❑ **Set Goals**—deciding, and then working, to make improvements in one's physical, intellectual, social, or emotional condition

Character Traits

❑ **Caring**—kindness and concern; demonstrated by helping and supporting friends, family, and others

❑ **Citizenship**—pride in one's school, community, state, and country; demonstrated by obeying rules and laws and by protecting the environment

❑ **Fairness**—treating others equally; demonstrated by sharing, playing by the rules, taking turns, and being a good sport

❑ **Respect**—consideration toward others; demonstrated by being polite, using good manners, thinking about the feelings of others, and showing respect for oneself

❑ **Responsibility**—doing what one is supposed to do; demonstrated by practicing self-control, completing tasks, and setting and carrying out goals

❑ **Trustworthiness**—being dependable and loyal; demonstrated by doing the right thing, telling the truth, and not lying, cheating, stealing, or breaking promises

© Harcourt

Tips for Using the Observation Checklists

- Survey the Chapter Organizer, the margin features, and the Chapter Review pages in your *Teacher Edition* to identify the Life Skills and Character Traits developed in a chapter. Then decide which of these features you will assess by using the checklists.

- Select several students to observe. Often your observations can be more effective if you focus your attention on only a few students rather than trying to observe the whole class at once.

- Don't agonize over the ratings. Students who stand out as particularly strong will clearly merit a rating of 3. Others will clearly earn a rating of 1. This doesn't mean, however, that a 2 is automatically the appropriate rating for the rest of the class. There may be students who have not had sufficient opportunity to display their strengths or weaknesses. In those instances, "Not Enough Opportunity to Observe" may be the most appropriate rating.

- Use the data you collect. Refer to your observation checklists while making lesson plans, evaluating your students' growth in health, and holding conferences with students and family members.

Student's Name _____

Rating Scale
- ☑ 3 Outstanding
- ☑ 2 Satisfactory
- ☑ 1 Improvement Needed
- ☐ Not Enough Opportunity to Observe

Dates

✔ Make Responsible Decisions
Skill Indicators: The student
- considers options, risks, and constraints.
- role-plays healthful decision making.
- makes wise decisions in everyday situations.

✔ Refuse
Skill Indicators: The student
- says *no* in a convincing way.
- suggests healthful alternatives to health-risking activities.
- uses facts to explain reasons for refusal.
- walks away if peer pressure becomes too great.

✔ Resolve Conflicts
Skill Indicators: The student
- explores options.
- listens attentively to others.
- deals with a problem calmly or makes plans to discuss the problem at a later time.
- walks away if a situation may become violent.

✔ Manage Stress
Skill Indicators: The student
- analyzes the cause of the stress.
- talks about feelings and seeks help if necessary.
- finds an outlet, such as exercise.

✔ Communicate
Skill Indicators: The student
- seeks help for problems.
- presents ideas clearly.
- fulfills the purpose of the communication.
- listens attentively to others.

✔ Set Goals
Skill Indicators: The student
- sets reasonable goals to improve or maintain health.
- makes an action plan to achieve goals.
- is disciplined in following a plan.
- evaluates the results of personal efforts.

© Harcourt

Student's Name _____

Rating Scale

3 Outstanding
2 Satisfactory
1 Improvement Needed
☐ Not Enough Opportunity to Observe

Dates

✔ Caring
Trait Indicators: The student
- shows concern for others.
- helps people in need.
- avoids hurting the feelings of others.

✔ Citizenship
Trait Indicators: The student
- takes pride in the school, community, state, and country.
- obeys rules and laws.
- cooperates with others.
- protects the environment.

✔ Fairness
Trait Indicators: The student
- plays by the rules.
- shares and takes turns.
- is a good sport.

✔ Respect
Trait Indicators: The student
- is polite and uses good manners.
- shows self-respect and self-confidence.
- accepts others who are different.

✔ Responsibility
Trait Indicators: The student
- practices self-control.
- expresses feelings, needs, and wants in appropriate ways.
- sets goals and completes tasks.
- is a good role model.

✔ Trustworthiness
Trait Indicators: The student
- tells the truth.
- does the right thing.
- reports dangerous situations.
- is dependable.

Student Self-Assessment

Researchers have evidence that self-assessment and the reflection it involves can have significant and positive effects on learning. To achieve these effects, students must be challenged to reflect on their work and to monitor, analyze, and control their own learning—beginning in the earliest grades.

HARCOURT HEALTH AND FITNESS provides three checklists to encourage self-assessment.

- The "Health Habits Checklist" on page 9 allows each student to do a self-assessment of his or her level of wellness. The checklist helps students target health areas to work on throughout the year.
- The "My Thoughts Exactly!" checklist on page 10 allows individual students to reflect on their work at the end of a chapter.
- The "How Did Your Team Do?" checklist on page 11 provides an opportunity for a team of students to reflect on how they did after they have worked together on a health activity or project.

Other opportunities for student self-assessment include Life Skills Activities and Building Good Character Activities, found as margin features in each chapter. Each focuses on one of the Life Skills and Character Traits noted on page 4. In addition, there are opportunities throughout the program to develop Personal Health Plans. These features allow students to focus on some area of their personal health that they would like to improve, set a goal for improvement, and monitor progress toward the goal. Personal Health Plans provide an opportunity for private self-assessment and reflection and should not be used for evaluation or assessment.

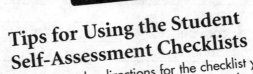

Tips for Using the Student Self-Assessment Checklists

- Discuss the directions for the checklist you ask students to complete. Be sure to communicate that there are no "right" responses to the items. This is important if students are to respond honestly.
- Tell students that they can use the back of the checklist for anything they may want to add, such as something they still don't understand or something they need help doing.
- Use the Individual Checklist to evaluate changes in students' perceptions and attitudes, rather than to determine their grades. Use the Team Checklist to evaluate and promote class growth in group skills.
- You may also wish to use checklist responses in conferences with students and their families. Invite both students and family members to help you plan activities for school and home that will motivate and support growth in health.

Health Habits Checklist

This quiz will tell you how healthful your daily habits are. Put a checkmark in the proper column. When finished, add up your score. Take the quiz several times this year and see how your health habits improve!

	ALWAYS	SOMETIMES	NEVER
Using Life Skills			
1. I weigh options and make healthful decisions.			
2. I say *no* if I need to.			
3. I resolve conflicts peacefully.			
4. I use stress-management strategies.			
5. I communicate with others clearly.			
6. I set goals for myself and work toward attaining them.			
Making Healthful Choices			
1. I eat healthful meals and snacks.			
2. I get enough sleep.			
3. I make time for physical activities.			
4. I avoid tobacco, alcohol, and drugs.			
5. I take medicines safely.			
6. I use safety equipment when playing sports and use a safety belt in a car.			
Getting Along with Others			
1. I have some close friends.			
2. I am a responsible family member.			
3. I work well with others.			
4. I apologize when I am wrong.			
5. I feel good about myself.			
6. I get along with other students.			

© Harcourt

Give yourself 2 points for each ALWAYS, 1 point for each SOMETIMES, and 0 points for each NEVER. Add up your score for each category.

8–12 points You Have Healthful Habits!	4–7 points You Need Improvement.	0–3 points Work to Do Better.

My Thoughts Exactly!

Decide whether you agree or disagree with each statement below. Circle the word that tells what you think. If you are not sure, circle the question mark. Use the back of the sheet for comments.

1. I understand the ideas in this chapter.   Agree   ?   Disagree

2. I found this chapter interesting.   Agree   ?   Disagree

3. I learned a lot.   Agree   ?   Disagree

4. I liked working on activities as a member of a group better than working alone.   Agree   ?   Disagree

5. I contributed my share of work to group activities.   Agree   ?   Disagree

6. I helped others at home and at school.   Agree   ?   Disagree

7. I am getting better at decision making.   Agree   ?   Disagree

8. I make my needs, feelings, and ideas known to my family, my friends, and others.   Agree   ?   Disagree

9. I focus more on my strengths than my weaknesses.   Agree   ?   Disagree

10. I practice good health habits.   Agree   ?   Disagree

Think about each question below, and write a short answer to each one.

11. What did you like best in this chapter? Tell why. _____

_____

_____

12. What would you like to learn more about? _____

_____

_____

How Did Your Team Do?

Read each item. Mark the number that tells the score you think your team deserves.

How well did your team	High		Low
1. plan for the activity?	3	2	1
2. carry out team plans?	3	2	1
3. listen to and show respect for each member?	3	2	1
4. share the work?	3	2	1
5. make decisions and solve problems?	3	2	1
6. make use of available resources?	3	2	1
7. organize information?	3	2	1
8. communicate what was learned?	3	2	1

Review your answers to 1 through 8. Then answer the questions below.

9. What did your team do best? _____

_____

_____

10. What can you do to help your team do better work? _____

_____

_____

11. What did your team like most about the activity? _____

_____

_____

© Harcourt

Portfolio Assessment

For Portfolio Assessment, students make collections of their work. Their portfolios may include a few required papers such as the Project Summary Sheet, Project Evaluation Sheet, and Individual Self-Assessment Checklist. Beyond these, students have the opportunity to add work samples that they believe represent their growth in health.

Portfolios
- **provide comprehensive pictures of student progress.**
- **foster reflection, self-monitoring, and self-assessment.**

The value of portfolios is in making them and in discussing them, not in the collection content itself. Organizers are provided on the following pages to help you and your students make and use portfolios for evaluation.

Getting Started with Portfolio Assessment

■ Introduce portfolios by explaining that artists, fashion designers, writers, and other people use portfolios to present samples of their best work when they are applying for jobs. Explain that the purpose of student portfolios is to show samples of their work in health.

■ Engage your students in a discussion of the kinds of work samples they might choose and the reasons for their choices. For example, the portfolio might include a written work sample, Activity Book pages, and a creative product. Point out that students' best work is not necessarily their longest or their neatest.

■ Discuss reasons for also including a few standard pieces in each portfolio, and decide what those pieces should be. The Project Summary Sheet (page 18), for example, might be a standard piece in all portfolios because it shows the student's ability to use knowledge and skills to solve a problem.

■ Another standard portfolio piece might be the Health Experiences Record (page 14), on which students log their independent health activities, including out-of-school experiences related to health. The Health Experiences Record can reveal student interests and ideas you might otherwise not know about.

■ Establish a basic plan that shows how many work samples will be included in the portfolio, what they will be, and when they should be selected. Ask students to list on "A Guide to My Health Portfolio" (page 15) each sample they select and explain why they selected it.

Tips for Assessing Portfolios

- At the end of each chapter, complete the Health Portfolio Summary (page 16) to help you review and summarize the contents of a student's portfolio.

- Use the portfolio for evaluating the student's performance in health and when holding conferences with students and family members.

- You may wish to send the portfolio home for family members to review.

Health Experiences Record

Date	What I Did	What I Thought or Learned

A Guide to My Health Portfolio

What Is in My Portfolio	Why I Chose It
1.	
2.	
3.	
4.	
5.	
6.	
7.	
8.	

I organized my portfolio this way because _____

_____

_____

_____

_____

Name _____ Date _____

Goals	Evidence and Comments
1. Growth in knowledge about health and safety	
2. Growth in using Life Skills and Character Traits: • make responsible decisions • refuse • resolve conflicts • manage stress • communicate • set goals • caring • citizenship • fairness • respect • responsibility • trustworthiness	
3. Growth in ability to locate, gather, organize, and communicate information about health	
4. Growth in ability to practice good health habits	

SUMMARY OF PORTFOLIO ASSESSMENT

For This Review			Since Last Review		
Excellent	**Good**	**Fair**	**Improving**	**The Same**	**Not as Good**

Chapter Tests

Using Chapter Tests

The Chapter Tests can help you find out how well your students understand, integrate, and apply the important ideas that are developed in each chapter. The tests are divided into two distinct parts.

- The first two pages of each test contain exactly twenty easy-to-grade questions that test basic recall, vocabulary, critical thinking, and analysis. They are designed to give you an easy way to obtain a chapter grade for the health content.
- The third page consists of exactly five thought-provoking questions that require students to analyze and synthesize what they have learned in the chapter. These are short-answer, essay, complete-a-graphic-organizer, complete-a-table, or label-a-diagram questions. These questions provide you with more in-depth knowledge of each student's learning and retention.

You will find answers to the Chapter Tests in the Answer Key (pages 74–85) of this *Assessment Guide* as well as in reduced form at the end of each chapter in the *Teacher Edition.*

Follow-up discussion of students' responses to test items is encouraged. Discussion gives students the opportunity to explain their answers. (Creative students may devise an unforeseen solution to a problem or apply concepts in a correct but unexpected manner.) Discussion also helps dispel any lingering misconceptions students may have about the topic.

Name _____ Date _____

Chapter Title _____

To Sum It Up

You can tell about your project by completing the following sentences.

1. My project was about _____

_____

_____

2. I worked on this project with _____

_____

_____

3. I gathered information from these sources: _____

_____

_____

4. The most important thing I learned from doing this project is _____

_____

_____

5. I am going to use what I have learned by _____

_____

_____

6. I'd also like to tell you _____

_____

_____

© Harcourt

Your Amazing Body

**Match each term in Column B with its description in Column A.
Write the letter of the answer on the line at the left.**

		Column A	Column B
_____	1.	A strong, hard body part	**a** organ system
_____	2.	A group of organs that work together to do a certain job	**b** growth rate
_____	3.	All the bones in your body	**c** tendon
_____	4.	Groups of tissues that work together to do a certain job	**d** skeletal system
_____	5.	These carry messages to and from your brain	**e** spinal cord
_____	6.	Groups of cells that work together to do a certain job	**f** cell
_____	7.	Nerves that run through the backbone	**g** bone
_____	8.	The smallest working part of your body	**h** nerves
_____	9.	A strong strip of tough material that attaches a muscle to a bone	**i** tissue
_____	10.	The rate at which you grow	**j** organ

© Harcourt

Name _____

Write the letter of the best answer on the line at the left.

_____ **11.** Your _____ is the tube that connects your throat to your lungs.
    A diaphragm   **C** trachea
    B esophagus   **D** stomach

_____ **12.** The main part(s) of your respiratory system are your _____.
    F mouth   **H** trachea
    G esophagus   **J** lungs

_____ **13.** The muscle under your ribs that moves to push air in and out of your lungs is your _____.
    A esophagus   **C** trachea
    B diaphragm   **D** stomach

_____ **14.** Muscles in your _____ push food from the mouth to the stomach.
    F diaphragm   **H** trachea
    G lungs   **J** esophagus

_____ **15.** The acids in your _____ break down food.
    A mouth   **C** trachea
    B stomach   **D** lungs

Write *T* or *F* to tell whether the sentence is true or false.

_____ **16.** The human life cycle is made up of three stages of growth.

_____ **17.** The mineral calcium helps keep bones healthy.

_____ **18.** Your nose and mouth are parts of your body's nervous system.

_____ **19.** The stomach, liver, small intestine, and large intestine are parts of the body's respiratory system.

_____ **20.** Humans grow at different rates.

21. Cross out the sentences that do **NOT** describe how the respiratory system works.

The carbon dioxide in the air in your lungs moves through the walls of the lungs to all parts of your body.

Your diaphragm works to push air into and out of your lungs.

Air you breathe travels from your mouth and nose to your esophagus.

Your lungs take oxygen from the air and send it to the rest of your body.

In each of the following items, underline the age range that best fits the description.

22. Mind and body grow a great deal; you learn to speak, read, and write.

birth to two   two to ten   ten to adult

23. You stop growing taller but your body continues to change.

two to ten   ten to adult   adult to senior

24. You grow quickly, and you might grow as much as five inches taller in a year.

two to ten   ten to adult   adult to senior

25. You need much attention but begin to become more independent.

birth to two   two to ten   ten to adult

2 Taking Care of Yourself

Match the words below to the sentences. Write the correct letters on the lines to the left of the sentences.

a eardrum	**d** cavity	**g** pores	**j** ear canal
b dentin	**e** bacteria	**h** plaque	
c consumer	**f** dental floss	**i** sunscreen	

_____ **1.** Even though these living things are too small to see, they can cause illness.

_____ **2.** Sound waves enter your ear at the opening to this ear part.

_____ **3** You sweat through these tiny holes in your skin.

_____ **4.** You use this special thread to remove plaque from between your teeth.

_____ **5.** Sound waves make this part of your ear move back and forth.

_____ **6.** Acid-producing bacteria cause this hole in your tooth.

_____ **7.** This is a person who buys a product.

_____ **8.** This protects you from the sun's harmful rays.

_____ **9.** This hard yellow material surrounds a tooth's pulp.

_____ **10.** This sticky material can build up on your teeth.

© Harcourt

Name _____

● **Write the letter of the best answer on the line at the left.**

_____ **11.** Wash your hands to get rid of _____ on your skin.

    A cells   **C** pores

    B bacteria   **D** skin cancer

_____ **12.** Tooth decay starts in the tooth enamel, goes through the dentin, and finally reaches the _____.

    F gums   **H** root

    G crown   **J** fluoride

_____ **13.** Plaque and food between your teeth can be removed by _____.

    A fluoride   **C** toothpaste

    B flossing   **D** mouthwash

_____ **14.** Placing something pointed, such as a pencil, in your ear could make a hole in your _____.

    F ear canal   **H** middle ear

    G crown   **J** eardrum

_____ **15.** A consumer is a person who buys a _____.

    A product   **C** grocer

    B advertiser   **D** dentist

Write *T* or *F* to tell whether the sentence is true or false.

_____ **16.** The main goal of advertising is to get consumers to buy the advertised product.

_____ **17.** You should brush your teeth at least twice a day.

_____ **18.** Sweat comes to the surface of your skin along the tiny hairs on your skin.

_____ **19.** It is best to stay out of the sun between 10 a.m. and 4 p.m.

_____ **20.** Fluoride is a chemical that damages teeth.

21. Look at the diagram of the tooth. Write the name of each tooth part.

| pulp | enamel | root | dentin | crown | gum |

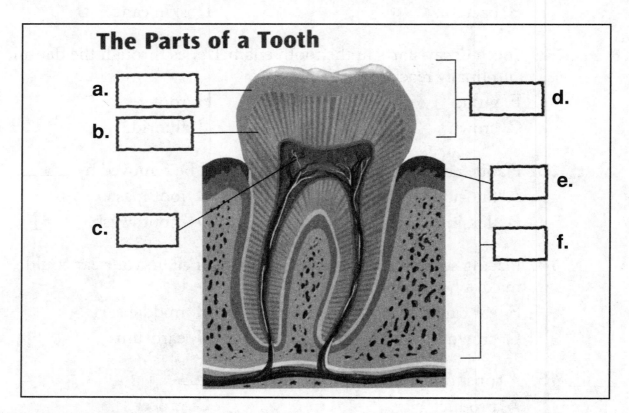

The Parts of a Tooth

a.

b.

c.

d.

e.

f.

Put the steps for flossing in order by writing 1 to 4 on the lines in front of the steps.

_____ **22.** Use your thumbs and index fingers to guide the floss. Gently push it between two teeth. Rub gently up and down, away from the gum. Rub near the gum line of one tooth and then the other.

_____ **23.** Pull out about 18 inches of dental floss.

_____ **24.** Remove the floss. Unwind it a bit to reach a clean part. Repeat for each tooth in your mouth.

_____ **25.** Wrap one end of the piece of floss around the middle finger of each hand. Leave a few inches between your two hands.

© Harcourt

3

Food for a Healthy Body

Match the definition in Column A with a term in Column B. Write the letter of the correct answer on the line at the left.

Column A

_____ 1. The things in food that help your body grow and get energy

_____ 2. A diagram that helps people plan a healthful diet

_____ 3. No longer safe to eat

_____ 4. The study of food and how it affects your body

_____ 5. A diet made up of healthful amounts of different foods

_____ 6. Foods you can eat between meals

_____ 7. Words that list the ingredients in a packaged food

_____ 8. The foods you eat and drink

_____ 9. A mineral used to make teeth strong

_____ 10. The things that are in a food

Column B

a balanced diet

b ingredients

c label

d nutrients

e spoiled

f diet

g MyPyramid

h snacks

i nutrition

j fluoride

© Harcourt

Name _____

Write _T_ or _F_ to tell whether the statement is true or false.

_____ **11.** It is healthful to eat just one kind of food.

_____ **12.** As long as you choose healthful foods, you can eat as much as you want.

_____ **13.** The widest stripe on MyPyramid is the Grains group.

_____ **14.** Snacks can be a part of a balanced diet.

_____ **15.** Fluoride is a vitamin.

Write the letter of the correct answer on the line at the left.

_____ **16.** Fruits and vegetables are foods that come from _____.
    A plants   **C** proteins
    B ingredients   **D** animals

_____ **17.** A protein is an example of a (an) _____.
    F ingredient   **H** balanced diet
    G nutrient   **J** snack

_____ **18.** _____ is an example of a healthful snack.
    A Soda   **C** Celery
    B Sugary cereal   **D** Candy

_____ **19.** A balanced diet contains _____.
    F one kind of food   **H** a good variety of foods
    G no snacks   **J** only expensive foods

_____ **20.** A food that smells and looks bad is probably _____.
    A spoiled   **C** a serving
    B balanced   **D** safe to eat

© Harcourt

Name _____

● **In each pair of foods, circle the choice that probably offers the best value.**

21. a large can of orange juice
a package of three individual containers of juice with straws

22. Super-Duper Whole Wheat Crackers
Store Brand Whole Wheat Crackers

23. Michael and Diego had fun playing baseball all morning. At noon they went inside to fix lunch. Why is it important for Michael and Diego to wash their hands before and after fixing lunch?

_____

_____

24. Keisha wants to choose a healthful after-school snack. Underline the snacks listed below that would be healthful choices.

candy	bagel	cookies
caramel popcorn	cheese	milk
orange	potato chips	sweetened cereal
apple	raisins	

25. Tara has decided to eat a balanced diet every day. Tell one reason this is a good decision.

_____

_____

4 Activity for a Healthy Body

Match each word below to a definition. Write the correct letter on the line at the left of the sentence.

a exercise	**d** cool-down	**g** strength	**j** ten
b warm-up	**e** safety gear	**h** flexibility	
c aerobic exercise	**f** mouth guard	**i** endurance	

_____ **1.** This kind of exercise makes your heart stronger

_____ **2.** How powerful your muscles are

_____ **3.** Being able to exercise for a long period of time without getting tired

_____ **4.** Any activity that makes your body work hard

_____ **5.** A way to get your body ready for exercise

_____ **6.** Clothing or equipment that helps protect you during sports or exercise

_____ **7.** Slow exercises after your workout

_____ **8.** A plastic shield that protects your teeth and gums

_____ **9.** How easily you can bend and stretch

_____ **10.** The number of hours of sleep a person your age should get

Name _____

● **Write *T* on the blank if the sentence is true. Write *F* if it is false.**

_____ **11.** A mouth guard can protect your shins when you play sports.

_____ **12.** It is important to warm up before you exercise.

_____ **13.** The Activity Pyramid can help you choose a variety of activities to keep your body fit.

_____ **14.** If you are injured, you should stop exercising or playing a sport right away, and tell your parent or another trusted adult.

Write the letter of the best answer on the line.

_____ **15.** If you don't get enough sleep each night, you could feel _____.
  A rested   **C** healthy
  B stressed   **D** relaxed

● _____ **16.** A person who can exercise for a long time without feeling tired has good _____.
  F flexibility   **H** endurance
  G strength   **J** aerobic exercise

_____ **17.** What should you do if you are injured while you are playing a sport or exercising?
  A tell a parent or coach   **C** keep doing the activity
  B act as if nothing is wrong **D** play a different sport

_____ **18.** What body part gets stronger when you do aerobic exercise?
  F heart   **H** stomach
  G feet   **J** hands

_____ **19.** How many hours of sleep do people your age need each night?
  A at least 12   **C** about 10
  B no more than 9   **D** between 6 and 7

● _____ **20.** Which of these is **NOT** an effect of getting plenty of rest and exercise?
  F feeling fit   **H** being healthy
  G feeling good about yourself **J** getting good grades

21. Draw a picture of someone following a rule for water safety, and write a sentence that tells about the water safety rule in the picture.

```



```

_____

22. Latasha said she does not exercise because it makes her tired. What would you say to Latasha to encourage her to start exercising?

_____

_____

23. Underline the sentences that tell ways to get enough sleep at night.

Don't eat much right before bedtime.

Run around or ride your bike right before bedtime.

Go to bed at the same time each night.

Be calm and quiet right before bedtime.

Drink soda right before bedtime.

Go to bed and wake up at different times each day.

24. Tim and Michael are planning a long bike ride. What are two rules they should follow to stay safe on their bike ride?

_____

_____

25. Justin has made an exercise plan. When you read his plan, you see that it does not have a warm-up or a cool-down. What could you tell Justin about warm-ups and cool-downs so that he will use them?

_____

Chapter Test

Keeping Safe

Write _T_ or _F_ to tell whether the sentence is true or false.

_____ **1.** A trusted adult is someone you don't know.

_____ **2.** When you ride in a car or a bus, you are a passenger.

_____ **3.** Wrist guards and kneepads are safety gear for skateboarding.

_____ **4.** Safety rules are rules made to protect you from injury.

_____ **5.** The safest place for children riding in a car is in the front seat.

Underline the word that makes each statement false. Choose the correct word from the box, and write it in the blank following the statement.

violence	safety rules	bully	stranger	trusted adult

6. Injury is anything someone does that harms another person.

   _____

7. A bully is a grown-up you know well. _____

8. You should just walk away from a passenger. _____

9. You can show that you are responsible for your safety by

   following hazards. _____

10. Never go with a trusted adult who asks you to help find a lost pet.

   _____

© Harcourt

Name _____

Write the letter of the best answer on the line at the left.

_____ **11.** Clothing worn to protect players from injury is called _____.

    A safety net   **C** safety gear

    B safety guard   **D** safety belt

_____ **12.** An important piece of safety gear for riding a bike is _____.

    F a mouth guard   **H** a helmet

    G kneepads   **J** elbow pads

_____ **13.** A place or a time that you may not go beyond is a _____.

    A safety rule   **C** hazard

    B limit   **D** passenger

_____ **14.** Harm done to a person's body is _____.

    F a danger   **H** an injury

    G a hazard   **J** a limit

_____ **15.** A danger that could lead to injury is a _____.

    A limit   **C** stranger

    B hazard   **D** driveway

_____ **16.** Someone you do not know well is a _____.

    F bully   **H** stranger

    G passenger   **J** trusted adult

_____ **17.** A person who hurts or threatens other people is a _____.

    A bully   **C** trusted adult

    B driver   **D** passenger

_____ **18.** Always stay more than an arm's length away from a _____.

    F bully   **H** stranger

    G trusted adult   **J** passenger

_____ **19.** The best place for small children to ride in a car is _____.

    A as a passenger   **C** next to the driver

    B in the back seat   **D** in their mother's lap

_____ **20.** When you buy a bicycle helmet, you should look for _____.

    F your favorite color   **H** the most expensive helmet

    G one that fits loosely   **J** a safety approval sticker

© Harcourt

21. Underline the actions you should take if a bully frightens you.

Ignore mean remarks.   Get help if the bully follows you.

Don't talk back or fight.   Yell something mean back at the bully.

Choose friends who stay away from bullies.

22. Cross out the descriptions of safety helmets that would **NOT** be good choices.

The helmet fits level on your head.   The helmet pulls off easily.

The helmet sits high on your forehead.

The helmet has a sticker showing it meets safety standards.

23. Kaarem is buying a skateboard. Tell what safety gear he should buy and what it will protect.

_____

_____

24. Adam moves closer to the stage at a concert to get a better look at the band. When he is ready to return to his place, he can no longer see his family. What should he do?

_____

_____

25. Serena's parents want her to walk home from school along Washington Street and then Pine Street. Serena's best friend lives on Main Street, so Serena would rather walk along Main and then Pine Street. What should Serena do?

_____

_____

Emergency Safety

Match each term in Column B with its description in Column A.
Write the letter of the term in the line to the left of Column A.

		Column A	Column B
_____	1.	Actions taken by people to cause a disaster	**a** hurricane
_____	2.	An object that can start a fire	**b** emergency
_____	3.	A storm with strong winds and heavy rain	**c** electricity
_____	4.	An event that causes great damage	**d** escape plan
_____	5.	A situation in which help is needed right away	**e** water
_____	6.	The steps to follow if your clothing is on fire	**f** disaster
_____	7.	A plan of action to follow in an emergency	**g** poison
_____	8.	A substance that can cause illness or death	**h** stop, drop, and roll
_____	9.	What you should **NOT** use to put out a grease fire	**i** terrorism
_____	10.	A form of energy that produces light, heat, and motion	**j** worn-out electrical cord

© Harcourt

Write the letter of the best answer on the line at the left.

_____ **11.** One natural disaster that cannot yet be predicted is _____.

    A a hurricane   **C** a tornado

    B an earthquake   **D** a blizzard

_____ **12.** A violent storm that forms over water and causes wind damage and flooding is a _____.

    F disaster   **H** hurricane

    G tornado   **J** blizzard

_____ **13.** The most important thing your family can do to plan for emergencies is to have _____.

    A escape plans   **C** fire drills

    B cell phones   **D** meeting places

_____ **14.** Electricity can cause electric shocks and _____.

    F disasters   **H** fires

    G flooding   **J** choking

_____ **15.** A strong windstorm with a funnel-shaped cloud is _____.

    A a blizzard   **C** an earthquake

    B a hurricane   **D** a tornado

Write _T_ or _F_ to tell whether the sentence is true or false.

_____ **16.** Home products can be poisons if they are not used the right way.

_____ **17.** It is best to go to a room with a window during a tornado.

_____ **18.** Poisons can't hurt you if you just touch them.

_____ **19.** You should hide electrical cords under rugs so people do not trip on them.

_____ **20.** Don't use a telephone during a thunderstorm.

© Harcourt

Name _____

Complete the graphic organizer by writing the steps below in the correct order.

> Stop, drop, and roll.
>
> Crawl out quickly.
>
> Go to the meeting place.
>
> Warn others.
>
> Call 911.

ESCAPING FROM A FIRE

▼

21.

▼

22.

▼

23.

▼

24.

If your clothes catch fire,

▼

25.

7

Preventing Disease

Write *T* or *F* to tell whether the statement is true or false.

_____ **1.** Asthma is a communicable disease.

_____ **2.** A fever is a symptom that you might have a disease.

_____ **3.** Abstinence from tobacco is a healthful decision.

_____ **4.** Bacteria and viruses are both kinds of pathogens.

_____ **5.** Exercise and a healthful diet can help prevent some diseases.

**Match the definition in Column A with a term in Column B.
Write the letter of the correct answer on the line at the left.**

Column A

Column B

_____ **6.** A sign that something is wrong in your body

a pathogens

_____ **7.** A disease that can spread from one person to another

b communicable disease

c vaccine

_____ **8.** A substance used to treat an illness

d medicine

_____ **9.** A substance used to keep you from getting a certain disease

e symptom

_____ **10.** Germs that cause communicable diseases

© Harcourt

Name _____

Write the letter of the correct answer on the line at the left.

_____ **11.** Which of these does **NOT** help prevent disease?

    A washing hands often   **C** eating a healthful diet

    B getting plenty of exercise   **D** getting very little rest

_____ **12.** Asthma and allergies are _____.

    F vaccines   **H** symptoms

    G noncommunicable diseases   **J** communicable diseases

_____ **13.** Fever, headache, and sore throat are all _____.

    A diseases   **C** symptoms

    B medicines   **D** pathogens

_____ **14.** Sneezes and coughs can spread _____ to other people.

    F pathogens   **H** vaccines

    G medicines   **J** noncommunicable
                          diseases

_____ **15.** _____ are pathogens that live in soil, on plants, and in water.

    A Bacteria   **C** Vaccines

    B Viruses   **D** Diseases

Match the definition in Column A with a term in Column B.
Write the letter of the correct answer on the line at the left.

          Column A   **Column B**

_____ **16.** Any disease that can't spread   **a** allergy
        from person to person

                              b asthma

_____ **17.** A disease that keeps the body
        from using sugar properly   **c** noncommunicable disease

_____ **18.** A reaction to something that   **d** diabetes
        is harmless to other people
                              e cancer

_____ **19.** A disease that makes
        breathing difficult

_____ **20.** A disease in which the body
        makes cells that aren't normal

Name _____

● Alicia has allergies. She is allergic to cats and dogs. What are two things that Alicia could do to cope with her allergies?

21. _____

_____

22. _____

_____

23. Maria knows that healthful eating can help her avoid disease. She is eating out with her grandmother. Circle the menu that is more healthful.

Menu #1
spaghetti with sauce
fresh green salad
apple
milk

Menu #2
cheeseburger
French fries
large soft drink
candy bar

Lena doesn't think exercise is important. She spends most of her time watching television and playing video games. What two reasons could you give Lena for exercising every day?

24. _____

_____

25. _____

_____

Medicines and Other Drugs

Match each term in Column B with its meaning in Column A.

Column A

_____ **1.** an illegal drug from the hemp plant

_____ **2.** a drug that can help you when you are ill

_____ **3.** an illegal drug that people sniff or inject

_____ **4.** an unwanted change that a medicine can cause

_____ **5.** a medicine that is safe only for adults

Column B

a medicine

b aspirin

c side effect

d cocaine

e marijuana

Write *T* or *F* to show whether the statement is true or false.

_____ **6.** A drug changes the way the body works.

_____ **7.** Too much caffeine can be harmful.

_____ **8.** Inhalants give off dangerous fumes.

_____ **9.** Over-the-counter medicines cannot be bought without a prescription from a doctor.

_____ **10.** The order a doctor writes for a medicine is called a pharmacist.

© Harcourt

● **Write *T* or *F* to show whether the statement is true or false.**

_____ **11.** A prescription medicine is a drug that must be ordered by a doctor.

_____ **12.** OTC medicines are for health problems such as sore throats, colds, and headaches.

_____ **13.** When you are trustworthy, you take medicines on your own.

_____ **14.** Inhalants can cause nosebleeds, hearing loss, and even death.

_____ **15.** Drugs make users do their best in school.

Write the letter of the best answer on the line at the left.

_____ **16.** When you refuse to use drugs, you _____.
    A agree to take them   **C** ask for more
    B can't find any   **D** say *no*

_____ **17.** Which of the following describes an inhalant?
    F drug that people smoke   **H** strong form of cocaine
    G fumes that contain poison   **J** antibiotic cream

_____ **18.** If you want to avoid caffeine, which shouldn't you have?
    A orange juice   **C** cola drinks
    B raisins   **D** yogurt

_____ **19.** Which is **NOT** an example of a side effect?
    F stomachache   **H** feeling dizzy
    G being very sleepy   **J** eating normally

_____ **20.** Who can help you solve problems with drugs?
    A a teacher   **C** a stranger
    B your younger sister   **D** kids who use drugs

© Harcourt

Name _____

Your family wants to post some safety rules for using medicine. Read the list below. Add two more safety rules.

Our Family's Safety Rules for Taking Medicine

- Keep medicines away from small children.
- Leave all labels on medicine containers.
- Never take someone else's medicine.

21. _____

_____

22. _____

_____

Lexie's older brother uses marijuana and cocaine. What two things could Lexie tell her brother about each of these drugs that might get him to stop using them?

23. Marijauna:_____

_____

_____

24. Cocaine: _____

_____

_____

25. Some older students at Melissa's school use drugs. Today they will ask Melissa to use drugs. Draw one way that Melissa can refuse drugs.

© Harcourt

Avoiding Tobacco and Alcohol

**Match each term below to a sentence. Write the correct letter
on the line to the left of the sentence.**

a addiction	**d** environmental tobacco smoke
b chewing tobacco	**e** cancer
c smokeless tobacco	**f** tar

_____ **1.** My neighbor has trouble breathing when he works hard. His lungs
are coated with a dark, sticky substance found in tobacco smoke.

_____ **2.** I saw a man put pinches of tobacco between his cheek and gum
and then suck on them.

_____ **3.** A high school football player wants to stop smoking, but it is hard.
He wants to stop, but his body feels a need for nicotine.

_____ **4.** A man on the subway put small wads of moist tobacco in his
mouth and chewed them.

_____ **5.** Kendra knows that using tobacco can cause this disease.

_____ **6.** The Chu family knows that being in a room full of cigarette smoke
can be harmful. They stay away from this kind of smoke.

Write _T_ or _F_ to tell whether the statement is true or false.

_____ **7.** Both alcohol and tobacco are drugs.

_____ **8.** A cigarette is the only type of tobacco product that has nicotine.

_____ **9.** Nicotine makes users want more tobacco.

_____ **10.** Alcohol causes changes in a person's body.

© Harcourt

_____ **11.** Some people who drink alcohol can't stop.

_____ **12.** Rules against smoking in public places protect people from ETS.

Write the letter of the correct answer on the line at the left.

_____ **13.** Children should not drink alcohol, because it _____.
- **A** prevents normal growth
- **B** is healthful
- **C** is NOT forbidden
- **D** tastes bad

_____ **14.** Drinking and driving can cause _____.
- **F** stomach ulcers
- **G** alcoholism
- **H** liver damage
- **J** crashes

_____ **15.** For some people, drinking alcohol can lead to _____.
- **A** new friends
- **B** alcoholism
- **C** smoking tobacco
- **D** a better job

_____ **16.** It takes alcohol just a few _____ to reach the brain.
- **F** hours
- **G** minutes
- **H** seconds
- **J** days

_____ **17.** What is one problem that alcohol use does **NOT** cause?
- **A** liver damage
- **B** trouble thinking
- **C** upset stomach
- **D** color blindness

_____ **18.** Which is a law that protects people from tobacco smoke?
- **F** no smoking in restaurants
- **G** smoking allowed anywhere
- **H** must be over 21 to smoke
- **J** must be under 18 to smoke

_____ **19.** How can you be trustworthy?
- **A** keep secrets from adults
- **B** make friends with everyone
- **C** follow family rules
- **D** use tobacco

_____ **20.** How does alcohol change your heart?
- **F** makes it strong
- **G** makes it beat faster
- **H** makes it feel upset
- **J** makes it stay in your liver

Write how tobacco use can harm the parts of the body shown in this diagram.

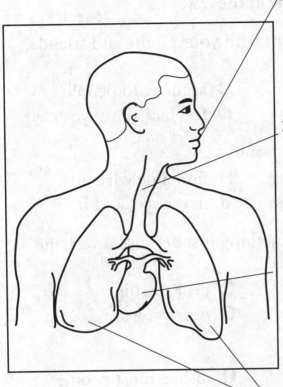

21. mouth: _____

_____

_____

22. throat: _____

_____

_____

23. heart: _____

_____

_____

24. lungs: _____

_____

_____

25. Friends of Devon's brother offer him tobacco and alcohol. What is one way he could refuse?

_____

_____

_____

_____

10

About Yourself and Others

Write the letter of the best answer on the line at the left.

_____ 1. When you have good relationships with your family and friends, it makes you _____.

    A feel good about yourself   **C** argue with people

    B make fewer friends   **D** feel bad about yourself

_____ 2. When you make a mistake, you should _____.

    F say mean things and walk away   **H** find a new friend

    G apologize and ask for forgiveness   **J** never speak of it

_____ 3. When friends want you to do something just because "everyone else is doing it," they are using _____.

    A peer example   **C** peer teasing

    B peer fun   **D** peer pressure

_____ 4. If you have compassion, you _____.

    F have a disease   **H** dislike most people

    G think only of yourself   **J** can feel what others feel

_____ 5. What is one way to be a good listener?

    A look the speaker in the eye   **C** watch television

    B notice people walking by   **D** keep talking

_____ 6. Family members have better relationships when they _____.

    F do their own thing   **H** respect each other

    G own lots of things   **J** argue often

Write _T_ or _F_ to show if the statements are true or false.

_____ 7. Air, food, and clothes are wants.

_____ 8. Body language can show your feelings for others.

_____ 9. Emotions are strong feelings that few people have.

_____ 10. Cookies are a need.

Name _____

_____ **11.** When you have self-control, you can control your unpleasant feelings.

_____ **12.** Eating well can help you handle grief.

_____ **13.** A good friend keeps a secret, unless someone is in danger.

_____ **14.** One way of letting go of unpleasant emotions is to forgive yourself or others for what happened.

_____ **15.** When you are responsible, people cannot count on you.

_____ **16.** You should treat yourself like an enemy.

Write the emotion that best matches the feeling for each situation.

> fear   grief   stress   anger

_____ **17.** Beth doesn't want to be best friends with Toni because Toni is telling lies about Beth.

_____ **18.** Pedro plays in his yard after school. Sometimes the neighbor's dog barks and growls at Pedro.

_____ **19.** Lauren's teacher told the class about an important spelling test tomorrow. Lauren forgets to take her spelling book home to study.

_____ **20.** Jaime's favorite cat was 18 years old and had been sick for a while. The cat died last night.

© Harcourt

21. Underline the situations in which you should ask for help.

You're afraid to go to school.   You feel sad a lot.

You can't sleep.   You get a great test grade.

You make a new friend.   Someone touches you in a way you don't like.

22. Look back at item 19. Write one thing Lauren could do to manage her feeling.

_____

_____

_____

23. Look back at item 17. Write what Beth could do to manage her feeling.

_____

_____

24. Draw a picture that shows ways that you and a friend could communicate respectfully. Include the use of body language in your drawing.

25. Suppose a family member hurts your feelings during a conflict. Write what you could do to resolve the conflict.

_____

_____

_____

Your Family and You

Write the letter of the best answer on the line at the left.

_____ **1.** A family is people who _____.

    A are all the same   **C** are related to each other

    B live on the same block   **D** have no connection

_____ **2.** If family members speak politely and respectfully to each other, everyone feels _____.

    F happier   **H** bored

    G angrier   **J** left out

_____ **3.** When parents divorce, they no longer _____.

    A have a family   **C** have any children

    B have a place to live   **D** are married

_____ **4.** A good way to show responsibility is to _____.

    F do only the hardest jobs   **H** do your job always

    G do only the easiest jobs   **J** do your sibling's job

_____ **5.** What does NOT happen when a family plays together?

    A The members talk and listen to each other.

    B The members learn to respect each other.

    C The members get to know each other.

    D The members fight.

Match each item in Column B with its description in Column A.

Column A	Column B
_____ **6.** value	**a** moving
_____ **7.** ritual	**b** providing food for the family
_____ **8.** family change	**c** picking up toys
_____ **9.** a child's responsibility	**d** eating with family every Sunday
_____ **10.** a parent's responsibility	**e** spending time together

Write *T* next to each statement that is true and *F* next to each statement that is false.

_____ **11.** One parent and one child are not a family.

_____ **12.** A parent reading a bedtime story to a child is a value.

_____ **13.** Taking a summer vacation each year is a ritual.

_____ **14.** Coping with change in a family is always easy.

_____ **15.** Changes in a family can cause many different feelings.

_____ **16.** The way family members talk to each other shows how they feel about each other.

_____ **17.** Not interrupting someone who is talking is a good listening skill.

_____ **18.** When family members work together, everyone has to do his or her part.

_____ **19.** All families are the same.

_____ **20.** Listening is one way to show respect for family members.

© Harcourt

Name _____

Read the paragraphs. Answer the questions in complete sentences.

21. Danny's job is to feed the family's dog each day after school. Danny's friends always want him to play after school. What might happen if Danny does not feed the dog before playing with his friends?

_____

_____

22. Ginger has her own bedroom for the first time because her older sister just went away to college. Ginger is very excited but also misses her sister very much. What can Ginger do to cope with this change?

_____

_____

23. Matt likes to play his favorite video game with his younger brother Joel. Joel gets frustrated because Matt plays the game so well that his turns last a long time. How can Matt help Joel with his feelings?

_____

_____

24. Arlo's father has a new job in another state. His family will move soon. How can the family members work together to deal with this change?

_____

_____

25. What are examples of activities that a family can enjoy together?

_____

_____

© Harcourt

Health in the Community

Match the words below to the sentences. Write the correct letters on the lines to the left of the sentences.

a littering	**d** pollution	**g** clinic	**j** groundwater
b recycle	**e** reuse	**h** environment	
c hospital	**f** community	**i** health department	

_____ **1.** Something that makes an environment unhealthful

_____ **2.** A place where people who are very ill or badly hurt can get medical treatment

_____ **3.** Water that sinks into the soil and fills gaps between rocks

_____ **4.** A place where people live, work, play, and go to school

_____ **5.** A group of health-care workers who serve a community

_____ **6.** A place where people with minor illnesses or injuries can get medical treatment

_____ **7.** Everything around you

_____ **8.** Putting trash in a place where it does not belong

_____ **9.** To use something again

_____ **10.** To collect used items so they can be made into new items

© Harcourt

Name _____

Write *T* or *F* to show whether the sentence is true or false.

_____ **11.** Loud noises are an example of air pollution.

_____ **12.** The environment is made up only of nonliving things, such as air and water.

_____ **13.** People who work for a health department are public health workers.

_____ **14.** People can be tested for diseases at clinics.

_____ **15.** A public health worker tests water, air, and soil for pollution.

Write the letter of the best answer on the line at the left.

_____ **16.** Used water combined with other waste is called _____.
A sewage   **C** groundwater
B air pollution   **D** rainwater

_____ **17.** A surgeon is a doctor who _____.
F works only at clinics   **H** measures water pollution
G performs operations   **J** studies diseases that spread

_____ **18.** Harmful chemicals and motor oil can cause _____.
A air pollution   **C** sewage
B noise pollution   **D** water pollution

_____ **19.** It often takes less money to make things from _____ materials than from new materials.
F reused   **H** recycled
G reduced   **J** polluted

_____ **20.** Traffic, jet planes, and construction equipment add to _____.
A air pollution   **C** sewage
B noise pollution   **D** water pollution

© Harcourt

Name _____

21. Explain how recycling can help the environment.

_____

_____

_____

Many things we use every day can be reused or recycled. In some cases, their use can be reduced. Complete the table by naming one way each item listed can be reduced, reused, or recycled.

	Item	Reduce, Reuse, Recycle
22.	newspapers	
23.	milk and water jugs	
24.	clothes	
25.	aluminum cans	

© Harcourt

Chapter Projects

Using Projects as Performance Assessments

The Chapter Project is a performance task that can provide you with insights about students' understandings, skills, behaviors, and attitudes about health. The project also requires the use of skills such as critical thinking, decision making, and problem solving. You can use the project to evaluate the performance of both individuals and teams.

Assigning the project at the beginning of the health chapter will allow individuals or teams to utilize information they are studying as they complete the project. You may also want to explain to students how they will be evaluated on their projects. Use the Project Evaluation Sheet for each project to explain the evaluation process and the rating system.

Distribute and discuss the Project Summary Sheet that is provided on page 18. You may wish to have students complete this sheet as they work on the project or after they finish it.

Table of Contents

© Harcourt

1

Your Amazing Body

Danger Alert!

Imagine that your foot senses danger. Write a story about the danger and how your brain finds out about it. Tell how your nervous system works with other body systems to help you avoid danger and stay safe.

2

Taking Care of Yourself

The Truth About the Tooth

Construct a display about teeth. Include a model that shows a cross-section of a tooth. Tell what kind of tooth it is, and label its parts. Explain how cavities form. Tell how you can care for your teeth every day.

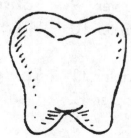

3

Food for a Healthy Body

Food for Thought

Gather information about the kinds of foods you need to eat to stay healthy. Cut out pictures of these foods from magazines, newspapers, and food products. Select groups of foods that show different ways to balance a meal. Paste the pictures on paper plates. Label the foods on each plate, and explain why each is healthful. Use the plates the class has made to make a food display in the cafeteria.

4

Activity for a Healthy Body

Add Variety to Your Life

Make a list of activities people do that provide exercise for their bodies. Next, make a list of exercises people do to build different kinds of physical fitness. Make up a game to remind players that there is a wide variety of things they can do to stay physically fit and active.

© Harcourt

5

Keeping Safe

Safety All Around

Make a collage showing ways to stay safe. You can use photos, draw pictures, or cut out pictures from magazines. Number each picture, and make a key that tells what each picture shows.

Wear a life jacket.

6

Emergency Safety

Help! Help!

With a partner, role-play what you should say in an emergency phone call for help. Your partner should give good advice to help you deal with the emergency. Ask classmates what else you could have said.

© Harcourt

Project Cards

7

Preventing Disease

Fight Those Germs

Make a bulletin board display of things you can do to avoid spreading germs. Make your own drawings, or cut out pictures from magazines and newspapers. For each picture, write a short sentence telling how the action prevents the spread of germs.

8

Medicines and Other Drugs

Medicines and Drugs: Helpful or Harmful?

Some drugs, called medicines, can make you feel better when you are ill. Other drugs can cause harm to your body. Make a poster that shows one or more drugs that people should avoid. Label the drugs. Write a slogan on your poster to communicate your message.

9

Avoiding Tobacco and Alcohol

Tobacco and Alcohol Affect Body Organs

Work with one or two classmates. Draw a life-size model of the human body on cardboard or drawing paper. On the model, show the body organs that are affected by tobacco or alcohol. Explain the harmful effects of these drugs.

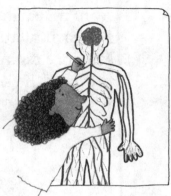

10

About Yourself and Others

How Do My Feelings Show?

Draw pictures of as many feelings as you can think of. Gather the pictures into a booklet. Write a description of each feeling, and add the descriptions to your booklet. Share your ideas about things you can do to get rid of uncomfortable feelings.

© Harcourt

Your Family and You

Things Families Do Together

Make a book titled *Things Family Members Do Together*. Include activities done for fun as well as jobs that members of a family might work on together, such as making meals. Make a plan for helping your family in new ways. Include your plan in your book, and share your book with your family.

Health in the Community

Useful Classroom Items

Develop a plan for reusing items in your classroom. Find out what kinds of things would be useful for art projects or other classroom projects. Decide where those things can be collected. Write a plan to share with other classes.

Project Title: Danger Alert!

Project: Write a Story

Objectives
- To identify the main function and parts of the nervous system
- To recognize the need for various systems to work together to keep the body healthy and safe

Use the indicators below to help you determine the student's rating.

Level 3

The student fulfills the purpose of the project in an exemplary way.

_____ Exhibits exceptional knowledge of the nervous system, its function, and its parts

_____ Writes a story that communicates ideas in a clear and effective way

_____ Conveys accurate information about the nervous system's reaction to danger

_____ Participates actively in discussions about classmates' stories

_____ Demonstrates good understanding of the need for body systems to work together

Level 2

The student fulfills the purpose of the project in a satisfactory way.

_____ Exhibits acceptable knowledge of the nervous system, its function, and its parts

_____ Writes a story that communicates ideas in a fairly clear and effective way

_____ Conveys relatively accurate information about the nervous system's reaction to danger

_____ Participates in some discussion of classmates' stories

_____ Demonstrates fair understanding of the need for body systems to work together

Level 1

The student does not fulfill the purpose of the project.

_____ Exhibits little knowledge of the nervous system, its function, and its parts

_____ Writes a story that fails to communicate ideas in a clear and effective way

_____ Conveys inaccurate information about the nervous system's reaction to danger

_____ Does not participate in discussion of classmates' stories

_____ Demonstrates little understanding of the need for body systems to work together

Rating _____

Teacher comments:

© Harcourt

2

Project Title: The Truth About the Tooth

Project: Make a Model

Objectives • To recognize differences in the structure and function of teeth
• To identify the parts of a tooth
• To understand how cavities form

Use the indicators below to help you determine the student's rating.

Level 3

The student fulfills the purpose of the project in an exemplary way.

_____ Creates a model of a tooth and labels its parts accurately

_____ Completely explains the steps in the formation of a cavity

_____ Demonstrates originality and creativity in the presentation of information

_____ Works alone with initiative or cooperatively with others

_____ Demonstrates strong commitment to using good dental hygiene

Level 2

The student fulfills the purpose of the project in a satisfactory way.

_____ Creates a satisfactory model of a tooth and labels most of its parts

_____ Adequately explains the steps in the formation of a cavity

_____ Demonstrates some originality and creativity in the presentation of information

_____ Usually works alone with initiative or cooperatively with others

_____ Demonstrates some commitment to using good dental hygiene

Level 1

The student does not fulfill the purpose of the project.

_____ Fails to create an accurate model of a tooth and label its parts

_____ Omits steps in the formation of a cavity or orders them incorrectly

_____ Demonstrates little originality or creativity in the presentation of information

_____ Lacks initiative when working alone or fails to work cooperatively with others

_____ Demonstrates little commitment to using good dental hygiene

Rating _____

Teacher comments:

3

Project Title: Food for Thought

Project: Make a Food Display

Objectives • To understand the essential types of food in a balanced meal
• To commit to eating better balanced meals

Use the indicators below to help you determine the student's rating.

Level 3

The student fulfills the purpose of the project in an exemplary way.

_____ Gathers information about a healthful diet from a variety of sources

_____ Organizes information to demonstrate a thorough understanding of the essential elements of a balanced meal

_____ Works alone with initiative or cooperatively with others

_____ Communicates ideas clearly and effectively through a food display

_____ Demonstrates strong commitment to eating balanced meals

Level 2

The student fulfills the purpose of the project in a satisfactory way.

_____ Gathers information about a healthful diet from one source

_____ Organizes information to demonstrate a reasonable understanding of the essential elements of a balanced meal

_____ Works alone with initiative or cooperatively with others most of the time

_____ Communicates ideas through a food display in a reasonably clear and effective way

_____ Demonstrates some commitment to eating balanced meals

Level 1

The student does not fulfill the purpose of the project.

_____ Gathers insufficient information about a healthful diet

_____ Fails to organize information to demonstrate an adequate understanding of the essential elements of a balanced meal

_____ Lacks initiative when working alone or fails to work cooperatively with others

_____ Has difficulty communicating clear, complete ideas through a food display

_____ Demonstrates little commitment to eating balanced meals

Rating _____

Teacher comments:

4 Project Title: Add Variety to Your Life

Project: Make Up a Game

Objectives • To broaden awareness of the variety of activities and exercises that help keep the body fit
• To understand the components of a good exercise program

Use the indicators below to help you determine the student's rating.

Level 3

The student fulfills the purpose of the project in an exemplary way.

_____ Creates a game that demonstrates a thorough understanding of all the elements of a good exercise program

_____ Discusses the game thoroughly with a health professional (or teacher)

_____ Works alone with initiative or cooperatively with others

_____ Communicates clearly and effectively

_____ Demonstrates strong commitment to following a daily exercise program

Level 2

The student fulfills the purpose of the project in a satisfactory way.

_____ Creates a game that demonstrates a reasonable understanding of all the elements of a good exercise program

_____ Discusses the game to some extent with a health professional (or teacher)

_____ Works alone with initiative or cooperatively with others most of the time

_____ Communicates in a reasonably clear and effective way

_____ Demonstrates some commitment to following a daily exercise program

Level 1

The student does not fulfill the purpose of the project.

_____ Fails to create a game that demonstrates a reasonable understanding of all the elements of a good exercise program

_____ Fails to discuss the game with a health professional (or teacher)

_____ Fails to use initiative when working alone or to cooperate with others

_____ Has difficulty communicating ideas

_____ Demonstrates little commitment to following a daily exercise program

Rating _____

Teacher comments:

5

Project Title: Safety All Around

Project: Make a Safety Collage

Objectives
- To understand good safety practices at home, school, and play
- To apply good safety practices in everyday life

Use the indicators below to help you determine the student's rating.

Level 3

The student fulfills the purpose of the project in an exemplary way.

_____ Gathers information from a variety of sources

_____ Organizes information to demonstrate thorough understanding of safety at home, school, and play

_____ Works alone with initiative or cooperatively with others

_____ Communicates ideas clearly and effectively through a collage

_____ Demonstrates strong commitment to practicing safety

Level 2

The student fulfills the purpose of the project in a satisfactory way.

_____ Gathers information from one source

_____ Organizes information to demonstrate reasonable understanding of safety at home, school, and play

_____ Works alone with initiative or cooperatively with others most of the time

_____ Communicates ideas reasonably clearly and effectively through a collage

_____ Demonstrates some commitment to practicing safety

Level 1

The student does not fulfill the purpose of the project.

_____ Gathers insufficient information

_____ Fails to organize information to demonstrate reasonable understanding of safety at home, school, and play

_____ Lacks initiative when working alone or fails to work cooperatively with others

_____ Has difficulty communicating clear, complete ideas through a collage

_____ Demonstrates little commitment to practicing safety

Rating _____

Teacher comments:

© Harcourt

6

Project Title: Help! Help!

Project: Role-Play

Objectives
- To build awareness of emergency procedures
- To demonstrate the ability to give important information in a telephone call for help and the ability to respond to a person seeking emergency help

Use the indicators below to help you determine the student's rating.

Level 3

The student fulfills the purpose of the project in an exemplary way.

_____ Gathers and contributes a great deal of information on emergency procedures

_____ Describes accurately what to do in an emergency

_____ Demonstrates thorough knowledge of what to say to get help in an emergency

_____ Communicates clearly and effectively

_____ Demonstrates strong commitment to following emergency procedures in everyday life

Level 2

The student fulfills the purpose of the project in a satisfactory way.

_____ Gathers and contributes some information on emergency procedures

_____ Describes somewhat accurately what to do in an emergency

_____ Demonstrates some knowledge of what to say to get help in an emergency

_____ Communicates somewhat clearly and effectively

_____ Demonstrates some commitment to following emergency procedures in everyday life

Level 1

The student does not fulfill the purpose of the project.

_____ Gathers and contributes little or no information on emergency procedures

_____ Describes inaccurately what to do in an emergency

_____ Demonstrates little knowledge of what to say to get help in an emergency

_____ Fails to communicate clearly and effectively

_____ Demonstrates little commitment to following emergency procedures in everyday life

Rating _____

Teacher comments:

© Harcourt

Name _____ Date _____

Project Title: Fight Those Germs

Project: Make a Bulletin Board

Objectives • To understand ways to avoid the spread of disease
• To demonstrate good health habits in everyday life

Use the indicators below to help you determine the student's rating.

Level 3

The student fulfills the purpose of the project in an exemplary way.

_____ Gathers information from a variety of sources

_____ Organizes information to demonstrate a thorough understanding of how germs are spread and how people can stop the spread of germs

_____ Works alone with initiative or cooperatively with others

_____ Communicates ideas clearly and effectively through a bulletin board display

_____ Demonstrates strong commitment to stopping the spread of germs and practicing good health habits

Level 2

The student fulfills the purpose of the project in a satisfactory way.

_____ Gathers information from more than one source

_____ Organizes information to demonstrate a reasonable understanding of how germs are spread and how people can stop the spread of germs

_____ Works alone with initiative or cooperatively with others much of the time

_____ Communicates ideas in a reasonably clear and effective way through a bulletin board display

_____ Demonstrates some commitment to stopping the spread of germs and practicing good health habits

Level 1

The student does not fulfill the purpose of the project.

_____ Gathers insufficient information or uses only one source

_____ Fails to organize information to demonstrate a reasonable understanding of how germs are spread and how people can stop the spread of germs

_____ Lacks initiative when working alone or fails to work cooperatively

_____ Has difficulty communicating clear, complete ideas through a bulletin board display

_____ Demonstrates little commitment to stopping the spread of germs and practicing good health habits

Rating _____

Teacher comments:

Project Title: Medicines and Drugs: Helpful or Harmful?

Project: Make a Poster

Objectives • To differentiate between helpful medicines and harmful drugs
  • To commit to avoiding dangerous drugs

Use the indicators below to help you determine the student's rating.

Level 3

The student fulfills the purpose of the project in an exemplary way.

_____ Gathers information from a variety of sources

_____ Organizes information to demonstrate a thorough understanding of the positive and negative effects of drugs

_____ Works alone with initiative or cooperatively with others

_____ Communicates ideas clearly and effectively through making a poster

_____ Demonstrates strong commitment to avoiding dangerous drugs

Level 2

The student fulfills the purpose of the project in a satisfactory way.

_____ Gathers information from more than one source

_____ Organizes information to demonstrate a reasonable understanding of the positive and negative effects of drugs

_____ Works alone with initiative or cooperatively with others much of the time

_____ Communicates ideas in a reasonably clear and effective way through making a poster

_____ Demonstrates some commitment to avoiding dangerous drugs

Level 1

The student does not fulfill the purpose of the project.

_____ Gathers insufficient information or uses only one source

_____ Fails to organize information to demonstrate a reasonable understanding of the positive and negative effects of drugs

_____ Lacks initiative when working alone or fails to work cooperatively

_____ Has difficulty communicating clear, complete ideas through making a poster

_____ Demonstrates little commitment to avoiding dangerous drugs

Rating _____

Name _____ Date _____

Project Title: Tobacco and Alcohol Affect Body Organs

Project: Make a Life-Sized Model of the Body

Objectives
• To recognize the harmful effects of tobacco and alcohol on the body
• To make a personal commitment to avoiding tobacco and alcohol

Use the indicators below to help you determine the student's rating.

Level 3

The student fulfills the purpose of the project in an exemplary way.

_____ Gathers information from a variety of sources

_____ Organizes information to demonstrate a thorough understanding of the effects of tobacco or alcohol on the body

_____ Works alone with initiative or cooperatively with others

_____ Communicates ideas clearly and effectively through a life-sized body model

_____ Demonstrates strong commitment to avoiding tobacco and alcohol

Level 2

The student fulfills the purpose of the project in a satisfactory way.

_____ Gathers information from more than one source

_____ Organizes information to demonstrate a reasonable understanding of the effects of tobacco or alcohol on the body

_____ Works alone with initiative or cooperatively with others much of the time

_____ Communicates ideas reasonably clearly and effectively through a life-sized body model

_____ Demonstrates some commitment to avoiding tobacco and alcohol

Level 1

The student does not fulfill the purpose of the project.

_____ Gathers insufficient information or uses only one source

_____ Fails to organize information to demonstrate a reasonable understanding of the effects of tobacco or alcohol on the body

_____ Lacks initiative when working alone or fails to work cooperatively

_____ Has difficulty communicating clear, complete ideas through a life-sized body model

_____ Demonstrates little commitment to avoiding tobacco and alcohol

Rating _____

© Harcourt

10

Project Title: How Do My Feelings Show?

Project: Make a Booklet

Objectives • To gather and organize information about emotions
• To develop techniques for controlling destructive emotions in everyday life

Use the indicators below to help you determine the student's rating.

Level 3

The student fulfills the purpose of the project in an exemplary way.

_____ Organizes information from a variety of sources

_____ Draws pictures that show at least four emotions

_____ Acts out how these four emotions feel

_____ Works cooperatively with a partner

_____ Communicates ideas clearly and effectively through drawings and actions

_____ Demonstrates strong commitment to understanding and controlling his or her emotions

Level 2

The student fulfills the purpose of the project in a satisfactory way.

_____ Organizes information from more than one source

_____ Draws pictures that show at least two emotions

_____ Acts out how these two (or more) emotions feel

_____ Works cooperatively with a partner most of the time

_____ Communicates ideas reasonably clearly and effectively through drawings and actions

_____ Demonstrates some commitment to understanding and controlling his or her emotions

Level 1

The student does not fulfill the purpose of the project.

_____ Gathers insufficient information or uses only one source

_____ Fails to draw pictures that show at least two emotions

_____ Fails to act out how at least two emotions feel

_____ Fails to work cooperatively with a partner

_____ Has difficulty communicating ideas through drawings and actions

_____ Demonstrates little commitment to understanding and controlling his or her emotions

Rating _____

Teacher comments:

Name _____ Date _____

Project Title: Things Families Do Together

Project: Make a Book of Ways to Help Family Members

Objectives
- To gather and organize information about the skills and responsibilities of the members of the family
- To develop a plan for helping family members in new ways

Use the indicators below to help you determine the student's rating.

Level 3

The student fulfills the purpose of the project in an exemplary way.

_____ Gathers information by interviewing each family member

_____ Organizes information to demonstrate a thorough understanding of the skills and responsibilities of each family member

_____ Develops a good plan for helping the family in new ways

_____ Communicates ideas clearly and effectively through a family book

_____ Keeps a daily record of efforts to help the family in new ways

Level 2

The student fulfills the purpose of the project in a satisfactory way.

_____ Gathers information by interviewing more than one family member

_____ Organizes information to demonstrate a reasonable understanding of the skills and responsibilities of each family member

_____ Develops a plan to help the family in new ways

_____ Communicates ideas in a reasonably clear and effective way through a family book

_____ Keeps an adequate record of efforts to help the family in new ways

Level 1

The student does not fulfill the purpose of the project.

_____ Gathers insufficient information or interviews only one family member

_____ Fails to organize information to demonstrate a reasonable understanding of the skills and responsibilities of each family member

_____ Fails to develop a plan to help the family in new ways

_____ Has difficulty communicating clear, complete ideas through a family book

_____ Keeps little or no record of efforts to help the family in new ways

Rating _____

© Harcourt

12

Project Title: Useful Classroom Items

Project: Develop a Plan for Reusing Classroom Materials

Objectives • To understand the importance of reusing materials in the classroom
• To demonstrate a commitment to reusing materials in everyday life

Use the indicators below to help you determine the student's rating.

Level 3

The student fulfills the purpose of the project in an exemplary way.

_____ Gathers information from a variety of sources

_____ Organizes information to demonstrate thorough understanding of a plan for reusing materials in the classroom

_____ Works alone with initiative or cooperatively with others

_____ Communicates ideas clearly and effectively through a plan for reusing materials

_____ Demonstrates strong commitment to applying the plan in the classroom

Level 2

The student fulfills the purpose of the project in a satisfactory way.

_____ Gathers information from more than one source

_____ Organizes information to demonstrate reasonable understanding of a plan for reusing materials in the classroom

_____ Works alone with initiative or cooperatively with others most of the time

_____ Communicates ideas reasonably clearly and effectively through a plan for reusing materials

_____ Demonstrates some commitment to applying the plan in the classroom

Level 1

The student does not fulfill the purpose of the project.

_____ Gathers insufficient information or uses only one source

_____ Fails to organize information to demonstrate reasonable understanding of a plan for reusing materials in the classroom

_____ Lacks initiative when working alone or fails to work cooperatively with others

_____ Has difficulty communicating clear, complete ideas through a plan for reusing materials

_____ Demonstrates little commitment to applying the plan in the classroom

Rating _____

© Harcourt

Chapter 1 Test
Your Amazing Body

page 19
1. g
2. a
3. d
4. j
5. h
6. i
7. e
8. f
9. c
10. b

page 20
11. C
12. J
13. B
14. J
15. B
16. F
17. T
18. F
19. F
20. T

page 21
21. ~~The carbon dioxide in the air in your lungs moves through the walls of the lungs to all parts of your body.~~
~~Air you breathe travels from your mouth and nose to your esophagus.~~
22. two to ten
23. adult to senior
24. ten to adult
25. birth to two

Chapter 2 Test
Taking Care of Yourself

page 22
1. e
2. j
3. g
4. f
5. a
6. d
7. c
8. i
9. b
10. h

page 23
11. B
12. H
13. B
14. J
15. A
16. T
17. T
18. F
19. T
20. F

page 24
21. **a** enamel; **b** dentin; **c** pulp;
   d crown; **e** gum; **f** root
22. 3
23. 1
24. 4
25. 2

Chapter 3 Test
Food for a Healthy Body

page 25
1. d
2. g
3. e
4. i
5. a
6. h
7. c
8. f
9. j
10. b

page 26
11. F
12. F
13. T
14. T
15. F
16. A
17. G
18. C
19. H
20. A

page 27
21. circled: a large can of orange juice
22. circled: Store Brand Whole Wheat Crackers
23. Possible answer: You should wash your hands before and after handling food to keep germs from spreading.
24. underlined: orange, apple, bagel, cheese, raisins, milk
25. Possible answer: By eating a balanced diet, Tara will get the nutrients she needs to stay healthy.

Chapter 4 Test
Activity for a Healthy Body

page 28

1. c
2. g
3. i
4. a
5. b
6. e
7. d
8. f
9. h
10. j

page 29

11. F
12. T
13. T
14. T
15. B
16. H
17. A
18. F
19. C
20. J

page 30

21. Picture should show any water safety rule. Answers will vary, but should name a water safety rule—for example: Never swim alone.
22. Possible answer: Exercise increases endurance. When you have good endurance, you don't feel as tired.
23. The following sentences should be underlined. Don't eat much right before bedtime. Go to bed at the same time each night. Be calm and quiet right before bedtime.
24. Possible answer: The boys should wear bike helmets when they ride. They should drink plenty of water before, during, and after their bike ride.
25. Possible answer: Warm-ups and cool-downs help prevent injury.

Chapter 5 Test
Keeping Safe

page 31

1. F
2. T
3. T
4. T
5. F
6. Injury; violence
7. bully; trusted adult
8. passenger; bully
9. hazards; safety rules
10. trusted adult; stranger

page 32

11. C
12. H
13. B
14. H
15. B
16. H
17. A
18. H
19. B
20. J

page 33

21. Ignore mean remarks.
    Don't talk back or fight.
    Get help if the bully follows you.
    Choose friends who stay away
    from bullies.

22. ~~The helmet sits high on your
    forehead.~~
    ~~The helmet pulls off easily.~~

23. Possible answer: Kaarem should
    buy a safety helmet, kneepads,
    elbow pads, and wrist guards.
    These will protect his head,
    knees, elbows, and wrists if he
    falls.

24. Possible answer: Adam should
    look for a police officer, security
    guard, or other concert official.
    He should explain that he got
    separated from his family and
    ask to be taken to the place for
    lost children.

25. She should take the route her
    parents chose and then ask if it
    can be changed.

Chapter 6 Test
Emergency Safety

page 34
1. i
2. j
3. a
4. f
5. b
6. h
7. d
8. g
9. e
10. c

page 35
11. B
12. H
13. A
14. H
15. D
16. T
17. F
18. F
19. F
20. T

page 36
21. Crawl out quickly.
22. Warn others.
23. Go to the meeting place.
24. Call 911.
25. Stop, drop, and roll.

7

Chapter 7 Test
Preventing Disease

page 37
1. F
2. T
3. T
4. T
5. T
6. e
7. b
8. d
9. c
10. a

page 38
11. D
12. G
13. C
14. F
15. A
16. c
17. d
18. a
19. b
20. e

page 39
21. Possible answer: stay away from cats and dogs
22. Possible answer: get allergy shots
23. circled Menu #1
24. Possible answer: Exercise reduces stress.
25. Possible answer: Exercise helps maintain a healthful weight.

Chapter 8 Test
Medicines and Other Drugs

page 40
1. e
2. a
3. d
4. c
5. b
6. T
7. T
8. T
9. F
10. F

page 41
11. T
12. T
13. F
14. T
15. F
16. D
17. G
18. C
19. J
20. A

page 42

21.–22. Possible answers: Take medicine only from a trusted adult. Have an adult read and follow the directions exactly. Tell an adult if you feel side effects from a medicine. Don't share your medicine. Check the date on medicine, and don't use if it's too old. Keep medicine on high shelves or in locked cabinets.

23. Marijuana: Possible answers may include any two of the following: This drug makes it hard to learn or remember things, speeds up the heart, causes breathing problems, makes it hard to fight infections, makes users nervous, and causes lung problems.

24. Cocaine: Possible answers may include any two of the following: This drug can make you sad, nervous, confused, angry, tired, or dizzy; can give you lung or brain damage; and can kill you with a heart attack or stroke.

25. Check students' drawings. Drawings might show Melissa ignoring the older students; saying *no* and walking away; saying, "I don't want to hurt my body"; changing the subject by suggesting another activity; or showing negative body language such as shaking her head.

© Harcourt

Chapter 9 Test
Avoiding Tobacco and Alcohol

page 43
1. f
2. c
3. a
4. b
5. e
6. d
7. T
8. F
9. T
10. T

page 44
11. T
12. T
13. A
14. J
15. B
16. H
17. D
18. F
19. C
20. G

page 45
21. Possible answer: Tobacco use can cause bad breath, stained teeth, cracked or bleeding gums and lips, and mouth cancer.
22. Possible answer: Tobacco use can cause coughing and throat cancer.
23. Possible answer: Tobacco use can cause blood vessels to shrink, the heart to beat faster, and heart disease.
24. Possible answer: Tobacco use can make breathing difficult, and it can lead to lung cancer and other lung diseases.
25. Possible answer: Say *no* and walk away; point out that using tobacco and alcohol is illegal for children; say that he's promised his parents not to smoke or drink; laugh and say, "I don't want to hurt my body"; check the time and say that he has to leave.

Chapter 10 Test
About Yourself and Others

page 46
1. A
2. G
3. D
4. J
5. A
6. H
7. F
8. T
9. F
10. F

page 47
11. T
12. T
13. T
14. T
15. F
16. F
17. anger
18. fear
19. stress
20. grief

page 48
21. These items should be underlined: You're afraid to go to school. You feel sad a lot. You can't sleep. Someone touches you in a way you don't like.
22. Possible answers: talk with a parent, teacher, or friend about her problem; call a friend and ask what the spelling words are; write a note to remind herself next time to take home books needed for tests and other homework
23. Possible answers: identify that she is angry; cool down; use an "I" message to explain her anger to Toni; listen to what Toni has to say
24. Students' drawings should indicate communication through words, actions, and body language.
25. Possible answer: Use an "I" message that tells how you are feeling and why; listen to the other person; talk about the conflict; find a solution that works for both of you; if you can't resolve the conflict, get help.

Chapter 11 Test
Your Family and You

page 49
1. C
2. F
3. D
4. H
5. D
6. e
7. d
8. a
9. c
10. b

page 50
11. F
12. F
13. T
14. F
15. T
16. T
17. T
18. T
19. F
20. T

page 51
21. Possible answers: The dog might be hungry. Someone else might have to do Danny's job. This might make other family members feel unhappy or angry.
22. Possible answers: Ginger can write or e-mail her sister. She can talk about her feelings with a parent or another trusted adult.
23. Possible answers: Matt can give Joel longer turns or extra turns when they play so that it is more fun for Joel. Matt could teach Joel to play the game better.
24. Possible answers: Family members will need to help each other with packing. The family members can talk about their feelings and listen carefully to each other's feelings.
25. Possible answer: A family can go swimming together, play games together, read stories aloud, go to sports games together, or go to the movies together.

Chapter 12 Test
Health in the Community

page 52
1. d
2. c
3. j
4. f
5. i
6. g
7. h
8. a
9. e
10. b

page 53
11. F
12. F
13. T
14. T
15. F
16. A
17. G
18. D
19. H
20. B

page 54
21. Possible answer: Recycling paper can save trees.

22.–25. Possible answers are given.

	Item	Reduce, Reuse, Recycle
22.	newspapers	Newspapers can be recycled and made into cardboard boxes.
23.	milk and water jugs	Plastic bottles can be recycled and made into trash cans and toys.
24.	clothes	Clothes can be reused by younger family members.
25.	aluminum cans	Cans can be recycled and made into new aluminum cans.

© Harcourt